TRINITY
COLLEGE LONDON PRESS

C000240907

Flute
Grade 3

Pieces
for Trinity College London exams

2017-2020

Published by
Trinity College London Press
www.trinitycollege.com

Registered in England
Company no. 09726123

Printed in England by Caligraving Ltd.

7.50

Feelings

Arr. Robert Ramskill

Morris Albert / Louis Gasté
(b. 1951 / 1908-1995)

4

Pièce pour flûte et piano

(Sicilienne)

Claude Arrieu
(1903-1990)

Waltz

Cecilia McDowall
(b. 1951)

Flute
Grade 3

Pieces

for Trinity College London exams

2017-2020

Published by
Trinity College London Press
www.trinitycollege.com

Registered in England
Company no. 09726123

Copyright © 2016 Trinity College London Press
First impression, June 2016

Printed in England by Caligraving Ltd.

TCL 015525
ISBN 978-0-85736-507-1

Feelings

Arr. Robert Ramskill

Morris Albert / Louis Gasté
(b. 1951 / 1908-1995)

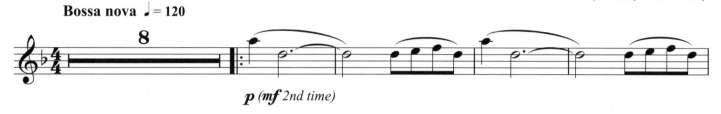

Pièce pour flûte et piano

(Sicilienne)

Claude Arrieu
(1903-1990)

Waltz

Cecilia McDowall
(b. 1951)

Seashore

Christopher Norton
(b. 1953)

The trees they do grow so high

Arr. Hywel Davies

Trad.

Piece no. 2

from *Twelve Easy Pieces for Flute and Piano*, op. 371

Wilhelm Popp
(1828-1903)

Mélodie Polonaise

Jules Demersseman
(1833-1866)

Four by Four

James Rae
(b. 1957)

Lovely Maiden

Traditional

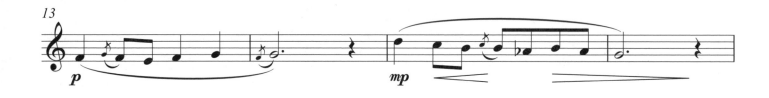

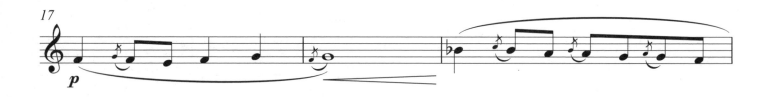

Seashore

Christopher Norton
(b. 1953)

Calmly ♩ = 84

Group A

The trees they do grow so high

Arr. Hywel Davies

Trad.

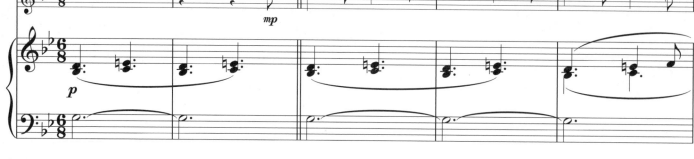

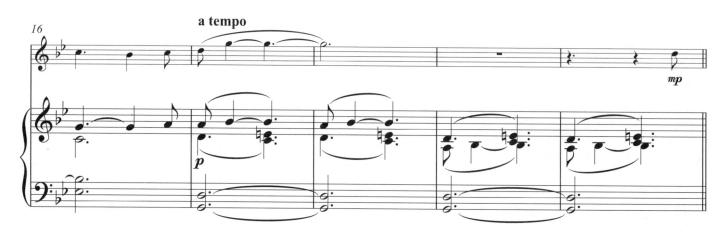

Piece no. 2

from *Twelve Easy Pieces for Flute and Piano*, op. 371

Wilhelm Popp
(1828–1903)